May You Always

35 Pop Songs Of Inspiration

Edited by Michele Baumann

Table Of Contents

May You Always

Words and Music by Larry Markes and Dick Charles
ASCAP

Bridge Over Troubled Water

Words and Music by Paul Simon

Moderate, not too fast, like a spiritual

Rubato

When you're wea - ry,—
down and out,—

feel - in small,
When you're on the street,

When tears are in your eyes,— I'll dry them all;
When eve - ning falls so hard— I will com - fort you.

I'm on your side. _____ Oh, __
I'll take your part. _____ Oh, __

___ when times_ get rough ___ And friends just can't be found,__
when dark - ness comes ___ And pain is all a - round,__

Like a Bridge O - ver Trou-bled Wa - ter

I will lay me down. Like a Bridge O - ver Trou-bled Wa - ter

Lean On Me

Words and Music by Bill Withers

Moderately slow

if I have things __ you need to bor - row __

for no - one can fill ___ those of your needs __ that you won't let __

show. __ You just call on me, broth - er, when

(Percussion)

you need a hand, __ we all need some-bod-y to lean ___ on. __ I just

15

I'll Be There For You

(Theme From "Friends")

Words by David Crane, Marta Kauffman,
Allee Willis, Phil Solem and Danny Wilde
Music by Michael Skloff

er know — me, no one could ev - er see — me.

F#m

Seems you're the on - ly one — who knows — what it's

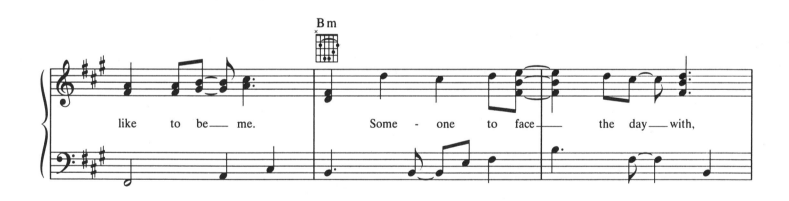

Bm

like to be — me. Some - one to face — the day — with,

D/A   G

make it through all — the rest — with, some - one I'll al -

That's What Friends Are For

Words and Music by Carole Bayer Sager and Burt Bacharach

Because You Loved Me
(Theme From "Up Close & Personal")

Words and Music by Diane Warren

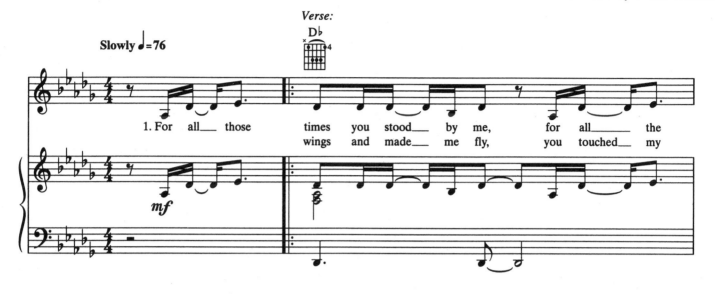

light in the dark,___ shin - ing your love___ in - to my___ life.____ You've

been my in - spi - ra - tion,_____ through the lies,___ you were___ the truth. My

world is a bet - ter place be - cause___ of you.___ You were___ my

loved___ me. You were___ my strength when I___ was weak, you were___ my

30

To Me

Words and Music by Mack David and Mike Reid

The Wind Beneath My Wings

Words and Music by Larry Henley and Jeff Silbar

On The Wings Of Love

Words by Jeffrey Osborne
Music by Peter Schless

on the wings of love. On the wings of love, on-ly the two

of us together flying high;

flying high upon the wings of love.

Yes, you belong to me,

Verse 2:
You look at me and I begin to melt
Just like the snow, when a ray of sun is felt.
And I'm crazy 'bout you, baby, can't you see?
I'd be so delighted if you would come with me.
(To Chorus:)

You Light Up My Life

Words and Music by Joe Brooks

lone in the dark, but now you've come a - long. And
Nev - er a - gain to be all a - lone

you light up my life. You give me hope,

to car - ry on. You light up my days and fill my

nights _____ with song. _____

The Greatest Love Of All

Words by Linda Creed
Music by Michael Masser
Arranged by Dan Coates

Circle Of Friends

Words and Music by Arthur Hamilton and Randy Goodrum

Let's form a cir-cle of friends,— bring ev-ery-one in—— and get to -

geth - er a - gain.— We know our fu - ture de - pends—— on

mak- ing this un - friend-ly world—— a cir - cle of friends.—

My hand in your— hand, her hand in his.—

What The World Needs Now

Words by Hal David
Music by Burt Bacharach

I'd Like To Teach The World To Sing

(In Perfect Harmony)

Words and Music by B. Backer, B. Davis,
R. Cook and R. Greenaway

65

It's In Every One Of Us

Words and Music by David Pomeranz

69

Touch A Hand, Make A Friend

Words and Music by Homer Banks,
Raymond Jackson and Carl Hampton

Verse 2:

Hey, what about you my friend?
Ain't it time to come on in?
We can find a better way.
Why don't you join us today?
Can't you feel it. . .

Verse 3:

It's been reflected in the attitude
Of other people just like you.
Reach out and touch a hand,
Make a friend if you can.
Can't you feel it. . .

Get Happy

Words and Music by Harold Arlen and Ted Koehler

Put On A Happy Face

Lyrics by Lee Adams
Music by Charles Strouse

doubt" look._____ Slap on a hap-py grin! And spread

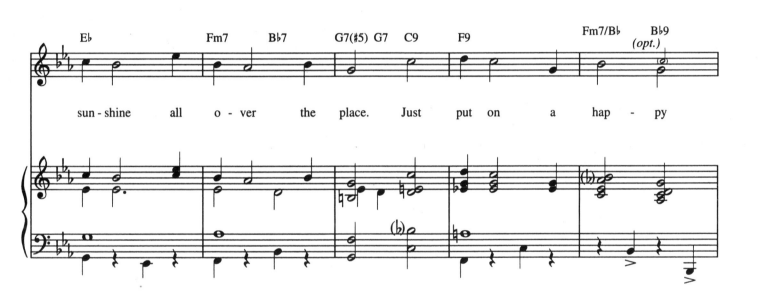

sun-shine all o-ver the place. Just put on a hap-py

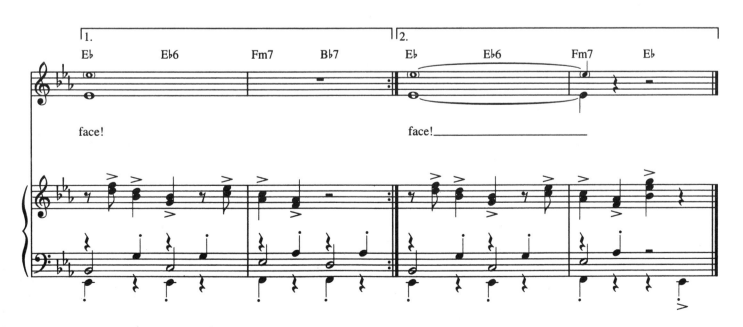

face!

face!_____

When You're Smiling
(The Whole World Smiles With You)

Words and Music by Mark Fisher, Joe Goodwin & Larry Shay

F7/C   F7   Bb   A7(b9) A7   Dm   Db+

- low   a - long,_____   One   could not   see,
- ed   to   rain,_____   Now   I   see   light,

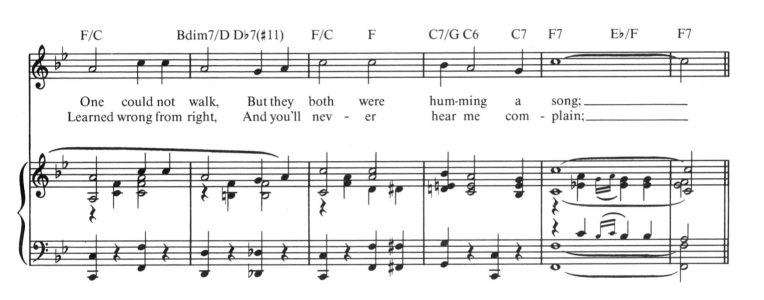

F/C   Bdim7/D Db7(#11)   F/C   F   C7/G C6   C7   F7   Eb/F   F7

One   could not   walk,   But they   both   were   hum-ming   a   song;_____
Learned wrong from right,   And you'll   nev - er   hear me   com - plain;_____

♩ = 80

Chorus: Tenderly

N.C.   Bb   Bbmaj7   G7

When you're smil - ing,_____   When you're smil - ing,_____   the   whole   world

p -mf

smiles with you,_____ When you're laugh - ing,_____ When you're

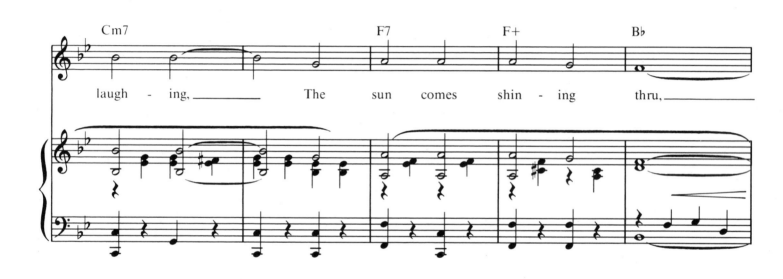

laugh - ing,_____ The sun comes shin - ing thru,_____

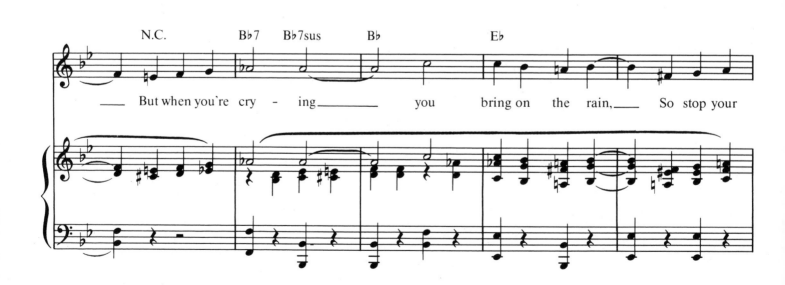

_____ But when you're cry - ing_____ you bring on the rain,____ So stop your

I Want To Be Happy

Words by Irving Caesar
Music by Vincent Youmans

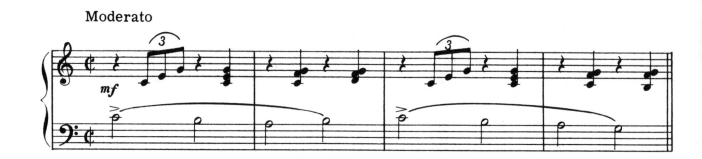

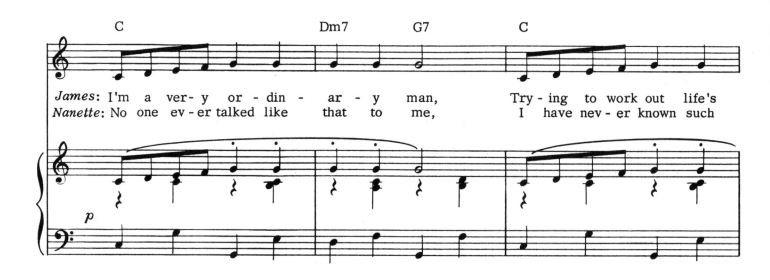

James: I'm a ver- y or - din - ar - y man, Try - ing to work out life's
Nanette: No one ev - er talked like that to me, I have nev - er known such

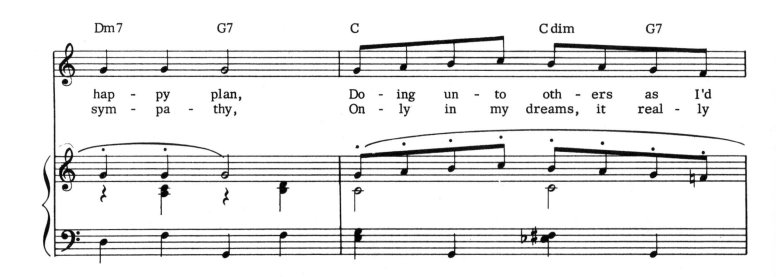

hap - py plan, Do - ing un - to oth - ers as I'd
sym - pa - thy, On - ly in my dreams, it real - ly

Tomorrow

Lyrics by Martin Charnin
Music by Charles Strouse

The sun - 'll come out___ to-mor-row, bet your bot-tom dol-lar that to-mor-row___ there'll be sun! Jus' think-ing a - bout___ to - mor - row clears a-way the cob-webs and the sor-row___ till there's none. When I'm stuck___ with a

I Can See Clearly Now

Words and Music by Johnny Nash

It's gon-na be a bright, bright_____ sun shin-y day. ____

Happy Days Are Here Again

Words by Jack Yellen
Music by Milton Ager

So long, sad times! Go 'long, bad times! We are rid of you at last. How-dy, gay times! Clou-dy gray times, You are now a thing of the past._____ 'Cause

shout it now!__ There's no one who__ can doubt it now,__ __ So let's tell the world__ a - bout it now__ Hap - py days are here a - gain!_____ Your cares and trou - bles are gone;_____ There'll be no more from now

What A Wonderful World

Words and Music by George David Weiss and Bob Thiele

I see trees of green, red ros - es too, I see them bloom for me and you, _____ and I think _____ to my - self

97

Feelin'

Words and Music by Paul Evans and Paul Parnes
Arranged by Frank Metis

The 59th Street Bridge Song (Feelin' Groovy)

Words and Music by Paul Simon

look - in' for fun and Feel - in' Groov - y. _____

Hel - lo lamp - post, what - cha know - in' I've come to watch your flow -

- ers grow - in'. Ain't - cha got no rhymes ___ for me?

Doot - in' doo - doo, Feel - in' Groov - y. _____ Got

no deeds to do, no prom - is - es to keep. I'm dap - pled and drow - sy and

read - y to sleep. Let the morn - ing - time drop all it s pet - als on me.

Life, I love you, All is groov - y. _____

Repeat and fade out

Day By Day
(From The Musical "Godspell")

Words and Music by Stephen Schwartz

Easy Waltz feel

mf

Fmaj7   **Gm7/F**   **Fmaj7**   **Gm7/F**

Day by day, ___   Day by day, ___

Bbmaj7   **Am7**   **Gmaj7**

Oh, dear Lord, ___   three things I pray ___

Em   **A**   **Em**   **A**

to see Thee more clear - ly,   love Thee more dear - ly,

clear - ly, ___ love Thee more dear - ly, ___

fol - low Thee more near - ly, ___ Day by day. ___

Day by day, ___

Day by day, ___ by day by day ___ by day. ___

Morning Has Broken

Traditional

Morn - ing has brok - en   like ___ the first   morn -

2. Sweet the rain's new fall, sunlit from heaven,
   Like the first dewfall on the first grass.
   Praise for the sweetness of the wet garden,
   Sprung in completeness where His feet pass.

3. Mine is the sunlight, mine is the morning,
   Born of the one light Eden saw play.
   Praise with elation, praise ev'ry morning,
   God's re-creation of the new day.

From A Distance

Words and Music by Julie Gold

111

Verse 2:
From a distance, we all have enough,
And no one is in need.
There are no guns, no bombs, no diseases,
No hungry mouths to feed.
From a distance, we are instruments
Marching in a common band;
Playing songs of hope, playing songs of peace,
They're the songs of every man.
(To Bridge:)

Verse 3:
From a distance, you look like my friend
Even though we are at war.
From a distance I just cannot comprehend
What all this fighting is for.
From a distance there is harmony
And it echos through the land.
It's the hope of hopes, it's the love of loves.
It's the heart of every man.

The River

Words and Music by Victoria Shaw and Garth Brooks

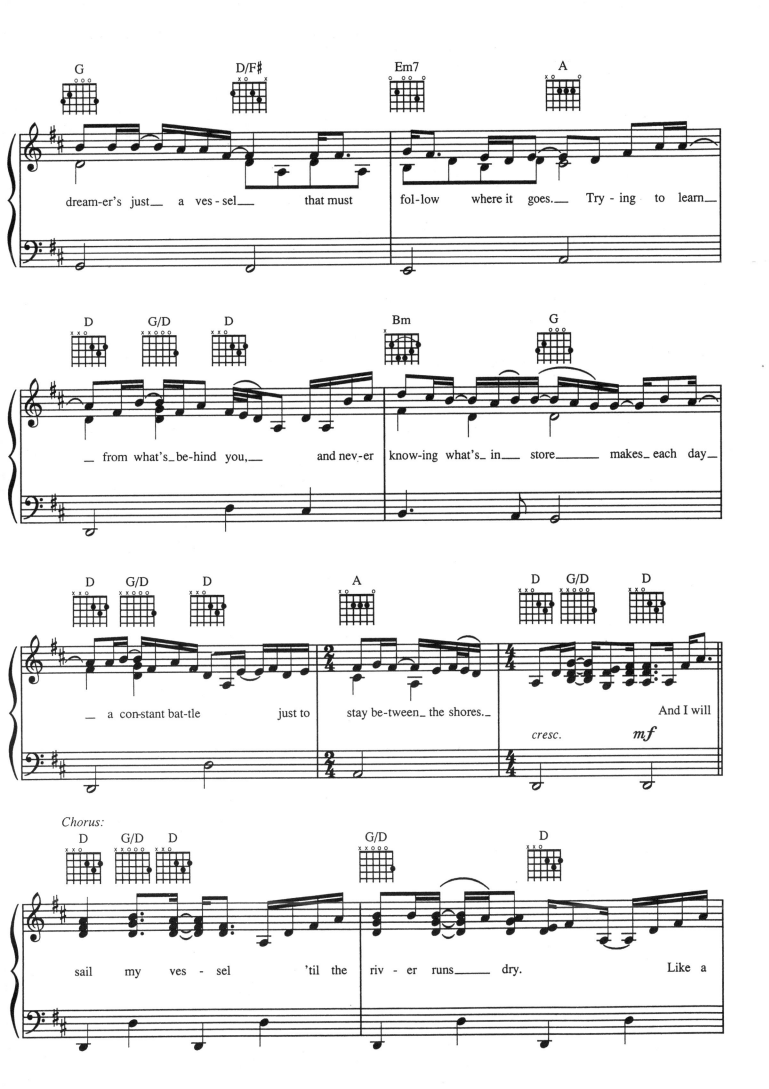

bird up-on___ the wind,   these wa-ter's are___ my sky.___ I'll___ nev-er

reach my des - ti-na-tion   if I   nev-er try. So, I will____

sail my ves-sel   'til the   riv-er runs_ dry.   *dim.*

D.S. 𝄋 ‖ 2.

2. Too man-y   And there's bound to be__ rough_ wa-ters__   and I

116

Verse 2:
Too many times we stand aside
And let the waters slip away
'Til what we put off 'til tomorrow
Has now become today.
So, don't you sit upon the shoreline
And say you're satisfied.
Choose to chance the rapids
And dare to dance the tide. Yes, I will . . .
(To Chorus:)

One Clear Voice

Words and Music by J.D. Martin and Marc Beeson

Verse 2:
I'm always searchin'
For which path to take.
Sometimes I'm so afraid
To make mistakes.
From somewhere inside me,
Stronger than my fears,
Just like the sound of music
To my ears, I hear...
(To Chorus:)

Angels Among Us

Words and Music by Becky Hobbs and Don Goodman

Spoken: I was walking home from school
(See additional lyrics)

on a cold winter day,

took a short cut through the woods and I lost my way. It was getting late

and I was scared and alone, then a kind old man took my hand and led me home.

123

Additional lyrics

When life held troubled times and had me down on my knees,
There's always been someone to come along and comfort me.
A kind word from a stranger, to lend a helping hand,
A phone call from a friend just to say I understand.
Now, ain't it kind of funny, at the dark end of the road,
Someone lights the way with just a single ray of hope.

(To Chorus)

The Keeper Of The Stars

Words and Music by Karen Staley, Danny Mayo and Dickey Lee

Now, I___ just can't___ be - lieve___ you're in___ my
I know___ I don't___ de - serve___ a trea - sure like

life. Heav-en's smil-in' down___ on___ me___
you. There real - ly___ are___ no___ words___

as I look at you___ to - night. }
to show my grat - i - tude. }

I tip___ my

mf

Chorus:

hat to the keep - er of___ the stars.

He Set My Life To Music

Words and Music by Kye Fleming and Dennis W. Morgan

Now——when I hear the sound of waves—— break-ing on the shore, or when I hear the wind—— rush through the trees,—— I have to stop—— and lis-ten.—— There's so much to thank Him for. I feel His har-mo-ny—— in ev-'ry-thing.——

Thank God For Kids

Words and Music by Eddy Raven

qui-et house With-out Big Bird or Mick-ey Mouse, And

Kool Aid on the couch, THANK GOD FOR KIDS

cresc.

CHORUS

THANK GOD FOR KIDS, there's mag-ic for a while

f

— A spec-ial kind of sun-shine in a smile Do you

ev-er stop to think or won-der why The near-est thing to

VERSE II

"Daddy, how does this thing fly?"
And a hundred other wheres and whys
You really don't know but you try
THANK GOD FOR KIDS
When you look down in those trusting eyes
That look to you, you realize
There's a love that you can't buy
THANK GOD FOR KIDS

Song Index